Grades 1-3

20 Thinking Questions for
SORTING TREASURES

Kelly Stewart   Kathryn Walker   Cynthia Reak

Creative Publications®

Acknowledgments

Contributing Writer: Susan M. Guthrie

Editor: Lynn Damme

Production Editor: Ann Roper

Classroom Coordinators: Kay Hatfield and Cindy Maynes Lopez

Creative Director: Ken Shue

Designer: Janice Kawamoto

Production Coordinator: Joe Shines

Production: Carlisle Communications, LTD

Illustrator: DJ Simison

Thanks to the teachers and the students of the many classrooms who tried out these activities. Their original work can be seen on pages viii–xi of this book.

ISBN: 1-56107-794-1
   3 4 5 6 7 8 9 10 . 9 9 8 7

Contents

THE CHANGING ROLES OF TEACHERS AND STUDENTS

In years past, the role of the mathematics teacher was to present students with rules and procedures, then give them problems to practice. The role of the student was to practice diligently in order to remember the information or procedures presented. Most time was spent on computation.

In today's world, mathematics is much broader than computation. Emphasis is on communication and complex problem solving. Rather than teaching specific rules for specific problems, teachers must help students develop thinking tools so that they are ready to meet the challenge of any new problem with confidence and enthusiasm.

It must be remembered that the purpose of education is not to fill the minds of students with facts…it is to teach them to think, if that is possible, and always to think for themselves.

—Robert Hutchins

What is the philosophy?

20 Thinking Questions is a series of 15 resource books created for teachers who wish to include investigative problem solving in their mathematics curriculum. Each of the **20 Thinking Questions** books focuses on students' use of manipulatives to solve problems having multiple solutions or solution methods. As part of the solution process, students write about their thinking prior to engaging in classroom discussions. Working with manipulatives gives students an opportunity to explore abstract concepts while manipulating concrete objects. Writing about one's thinking challenges students to clarify their ideas and provides teachers with insights into each student's thinking and level of understanding.

Your role as teacher is to pose a problem and then to encourage students to follow their own logical path in finding solutions that make sense to them. Greater emphasis is placed on the students' reaching an understanding rather than on them finding a correct answer.

How is this book organized?

Each book contains 20 questions emphasizing problem solving using a specific manipulative. In general, questions in each book are arranged from easiest to most difficult. However, depending on your students' backgrounds and prior experiences, you may find a different ordering of questions more appropriate for your class. Feel free to select those questions that best fit your students' abilities and interests.

When should I use these questions?

You can use **20 Thinking Questions** in a variety of ways, but we suggest that you use the questions in this book to create a "thinking strand" within your current curriculum. Most questions will take one, perhaps two, class periods to complete. Try one question every other week or choose another book in the series to provide enough questions for each week of the school year.

How is each Question organized?

The format of each question in this book is clear and easy to follow. The four-page question layout gives you all the information you need to help facilitate student learning.

The **QUESTION STATEMENT** lets you know what is being asked of students. Review these statements to help you decide if the question is appropriate for the developmental level of your students. You may find that you need to review concepts prior to introducing a question.

MATERIALS tells you at a glance what you need to prepare for the day's lesson.

INTRODUCING THE QUESTION walks you through an appropriate whole-class activity or discussion. It provides you with the necessary definitions to review prior to starting the question or gives you a simpler question to do as a class together.

Students will approach problems in many different ways. Some students may have difficulty understanding how to start while other students may finish very quickly. **WHAT SHOULD YOU DO IF...** offers you tips on what you should do if your students perform in a certain way.

What can you expect from your students? There isn't one right answer or solution method. **WHAT YOU MIGHT SEE** will give you some sample answers or solution methods. Don't expect your students to come up with some or all of these examples. Each student is different, and the think-

ing that emerges will range widely. The point is for you to become aware of the diversity in your classroom.

Has the student accomplished the expected outcomes? **WHAT TO LOOK FOR IN STUDENT'S WORK** tells you what to look for, helping you assess each student's work.

To enhance the learning potential of each question, give students time to discuss and to share the variety of solution methods they found. This is the time to post students' recordings or to let the class walk around and view each other's work.

QUESTIONS FOR DISCUSSION lists several open-ended questions that you can use to stimulate class discussion. If your class takes an interesting detour, go with it! The key is to let students explain their thinking.

Students will learn a lot from the class discussion, exchanging ideas and reformulating their own thinking. The **JOURNAL REFLECTION** gives students a chance to write about this thinking. It reflects new information and understanding students may glean from actively talking with their classmates. This writing is an extension of the writing students do in the process of answering the question, where they clarify their thinking of their solution. The Journal Reflection takes it a step further, allowing students to reflect on and to assess what they have learned. Choose the one Journal Reflection question that best fits your needs.

How should I organize my class?

During the course of each question's exploration, the class will be organized in different ways. You will meet with the group as a whole to introduce the question and for the follow-up discussion after students have worked on their solutions. Students will work with a partner or in a group to explore and to answer each question. As a culmination to the day's investigation, students will work individually to answer a journal reflection question.

How should I organize the manipulatives?

The complete manipulative kit for **20 Thinking Questions for Sorting Treasures** is designed to provide sufficient materials for 16 pairs of students. Included in the kit are 2 tubs each of the following Treasures: shells, creepy crawlers, tiles, and buttons. The exact type and number of Treasures each pair will need varies according to the question posed. You may want to have parents or older students help you prepare materials ahead of time as specified in the materials list for each question.

If your students are using a manipulative for the first time, allow them a period of free exploration to become familiar with the materials so they will be ready to focus on a question's solution rather than on the workings of the manipulative.

What about assessment?

If you choose to assess your students' work, there are a variety of approaches you can use. Having students keep a portfolio of their work will allow you and your students to identify growth in thinking, in problem solving, and in writing about their thinking. Observing and talking with students while they work will give you insights into their level of understanding, their confidence in approaching open-ended problems, and their ability to interact with others.

If you prefer to do a more formal assessment of students' work, the "What to Look for in Student's Work" questions will serve as a guide to help you evaluate each student's response. The Journal Reflection questions will give you insights into your students' attitudes about math.

The range of student abilities and responses will vary widely on these questions depending on each student's level of development.

A Thinking Question in Action

Mrs. Likens presents this question to her first grade class:

HOW CAN YOU SORT YOUR TREASURES?

Take out your Treasures. How can you sort them into piles of Treasures that are alike? Tell how you sorted them. Use pictures, words, and numbers to make a report. Show how many Treasures are in each group.

Each pair of students receives a group of Sorting Treasures and paper, pencils, and crayons for recording. To introduce the question, Mrs. Likens tells the students to work with their partner and to sort the Treasures into groups that are alike in some way.

After pairs have had some time to sort their Treasures, Mrs. Likens reminds the class that their job is to make a Treasure Report. **Tell how you sorted your Treasures. Use pictures, words, and numbers to make a report. Show how many Treasures are in each group.**

As Students Begin to Work

Mrs. Likens walks around the room, watching and listening. She notices some students making groups that do not seem to have a common attribute. She sits next to these students and asks them to explain their reasons for making groups. They have many reasons such as, "because these all make a star, because these are my favorites, because these are disgusting!" Mrs. Likens knows that these primitive sorting rules precede the ability to sort more consistently by a common attribute. She sees that these students do have a plan in mind even though it is difficult to discern at first.

Two other students choose to sort their buttons by size and they mean actual size! They put together buttons that are exactly the same size and then arrange those groups from smallest to largest buttons. This creates many, many groups often with only one or two buttons in a group. Mrs. Likens resists the temptation to suggest a three group system of small, medium, and large. Even though these students will have difficulty creating a report, she sees from their excitement that they have created a valuable experience for themselves.

Helena and Ann decide to trace their tiles to show their work. This produced a very simple and clear record of tiles sorted by shape. This way of reporting worked well for them and required no words.

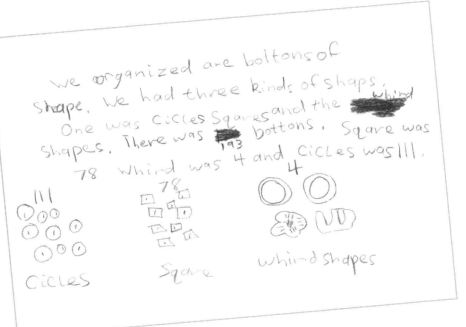

Everett and William had a lot more to say about the way they sorted their buttons. Mrs. Likens was interested to know that these two boys were able to total 111, 78, and 4 to get 193. They calculated and re-calculated several times to be sure of this number.

Jonathan drew all of his buttons and numbered them. Even though it is difficult to know Jonathan's sorting scheme (number of holes and design seem to play a part as well as "coloer"), he is making an attempt to communicate his findings.

ASKING EFFECTIVE QUESTIONS

Talking about ideas is an important aspect of creating confident mathematical thinkers. While students are working and during class discussions, it is important that your questioning style encourages students to think and to talk about their thinking.

■ ASK OPEN-ENDED QUESTIONS.

Avoid questions with simple answers, especially *yes* or *no*.

■ ALLOW TIME FOR EVERYONE TO THINK.

Ask a question and say, *Talk to your partner for a few minutes and be ready with an idea.* This encourages everyone to think about the question instead of relying on the "quick" students to do all the talking.

■ ENCOURAGE STUDENTS TO TALK TO EACH OTHER.

A discussion is a back and forth conversation. Get your students talking to each other, not responding to you.

■ TAKE ON THE ROLE OF THE FRIENDLY SKEPTIC.

Respond equally to right and wrong answers, saying, *Well, I'm not sure...what do the rest of you think?* Let the rightness or wrongness of answers come from the class, not from you.

■ CHALLENGE STUDENTS TO ASK THEIR OWN QUESTIONS.

Pushing beyond the original question to new questions and answers is an important move toward higher-order thinking. Ask, *What is another question you could ask about this?* Take time to explore some of these student generated questions.

■ GIVE GOOD THINKING TIME TO DEVELOP.

Include thinking questions and good class discussions in your curriculum throughout the year. You will see an amazing change in your students as their confidence soars!

Questions for Discussion

After the students finish their reports, it is time for a class discussion.

- **How did you sort your Treasures? How many Treasures were in each group?**
- **Did anyone sort the Treasures in a different way? Tell what you did.**

Mrs. Likens wants her students to begin to understand the importance of making reports that will communicate to others. She knows that this ability is one that takes many years to develop fully, but she wants her first graders to take the beginning steps. She asks her students to trade reports with another pair and then try to tell about each other's reports. Being careful not to allow criticism, students talk about what they can know and what they cannot know as they look at these reports.

Journal Reflection

Following the class discussion, Mrs. Likens asks her students to write in their math journals. The question she chooses is:

Suppose you were going to sort your Treasures in another way. How would you do it?

I will chose creppy critlrs because they abe so creppy and scary.

Journal Reflectonc

Next time I sort treasures I will chose tiels becayse it looks neqt. Even it is easy.

Mrs. Likens intended the question to mean, "Suppose you were going to sort the Treasures you just used again. In what different way would you sort them?" In true first grade style, everyone answered the question they heard which was, "Which of the other exciting Treasures would you like to work with next?"

Journal Reflections

Next time I sort treasures, I will chose ~~this~~ ~~shell~~ ~~because~~ ~~a~~ shell because it easy to sort

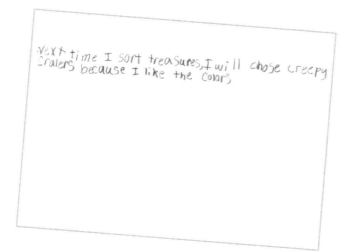

Next time I sort treasures, I will chose creepy crawlers because I like the colors.

Mrs. Likens decides to repeat this activity several more times over the next few weeks. It is obvious that the students are looking forward to working with other sets of Treasures! It will be interesting to see how their reports improve with more experience.

WRITING ABOUT MATHEMATICAL THINKING

Just as talking about thinking is important so is writing about thinking. The ability to explain ideas and findings to others is a critical tool for a future in which good communication continues to be a valued skill.

■ HAVE STUDENTS RECORD ON BLANK PAPER.

Organizing ideas and putting them on paper is an important part of solving any problem. Prepared worksheets do half of the work for students.

■ OBSERVE THE UNIQUENESS OF EACH STUDENT'S WORK.

When students are challenged to solve a problem in their own way and to report in their own way, each recording will be unique.

■ TAKE THE TIME TO COMMENT ON STUDENTS' WRITING.

Your comments will encourage students to improve their writing. Ask questions and give suggestions instead of making corrections.

■ USE PAIR AS WELL AS INDIVIDUAL REPORTS.

Working in pairs to solve and to discuss problems is often a good model. Reporting findings and ideas, however, should sometimes be done together, sometimes alone.

■ ASK STUDENTS TO REVISE THEIR WORK AT TIMES.

Let some writing be informal, a way of collecting ideas. Other times, have students revise their reports, making them ready to show to parents or to display in the hallway or in class booklets.

■ LET STUDENTS REPORT FROM OTHERS' RECORDINGS.

For another view of the importance of good communication, have students trade papers and report to the class about another pair's work using only their written report.

About the 20 Thinking Questions Series

20 Thinking Questions is a series of 15 books created to promote good mathematical thinking in primary through middle grade classrooms. Each book focuses on one manipulative and the many interesting questions that can be explored using that manipulative. Each book has a companion kit of manipulatives. If you and your students have enjoyed thinking about the questions in this book, try some of the other books! See a current Creative Publications catalog for prices.

Primary

20 Thinking Questions for Pattern Blocks, 31300
Classroom Kit, 31365
20 Thinking Questions for LinkerCubes, 31301
Classroom Kit, 31366
20 Thinking Questions for Base Ten Blocks, 31302
Classroom Kit, 31367
20 Thinking Questions for Shapes and Sizes Attribute Pieces, 31303
Classroom Kit, 31368
20 Thinking Questions for Sorting Treasures, 31304
Classroom Kit, 31369

Intermediate

20 Thinking Questions for Pattern Blocks, 31305
Classroom Kit, 31370
20 Thinking Questions for Rainbow Cubes, 31306
Classroom Kit, 31371
20 Thinking Questions for Base Ten Blocks, 31307
Classroom Kit, 31372
20 Thinking Questions for Fraction Circles, 31308
Classroom Kit, 31373
20 Thinking Questions for Geoboards, 31309
Classroom Kit, 31374

Middle School

20 Thinking Questions for Pattern Blocks, 31310
Classroom Kit, 31375
20 Thinking Questions for Rainbow Cubes, 31311
Classroom Kit, 31376
20 Thinking Questions for Base Ten Blocks, 31312
Classroom Kit, 31377
20 Thinking Questions for Fraction Circles, 31313
Classroom Kit, 31378
20 Thinking Questions for Geoboards, 31314
Classroom Kit, 31379

20 Thinking Questions for
SORTING TREASURES

1 How can you sort your Treasures?

Take out your Treasures. How can you sort them into piles of Treasures that are alike? Tell how you sorted them. Use pictures, words, and numbers to make a report. Show how many Treasures are in each group.

MATERIALS

For each pair of students

- ■ Sorting Treasures (approximately 50 of one kind)
- ■ paper, pencils, and crayons for recording

INTRODUCING THE QUESTION

1   Tell students they will be sorting their Treasures into groups of Treasures that are alike. **Take out your Treasures. Decide with your partner on a way to sort them. How can you sort your Treasures into piles or groups of Treasures that are alike?**

2   When partners finish sorting, they should count the number of Treasures in each group and make a report. **Tell how you sorted your Treasures. Use pictures, words, and numbers to make a report. Show how many Treasures are in each group.**

WHAT SHOULD YOU DO IF . . .

► Some students pick a sorting method that creates many piles or a method that creates only two piles?

This is okay. Be sure students can explain clearly what their sorting method is. It will be beneficial later during the class discussion to talk about why some sorting methods create many piles and other methods create only two piles.

► Some students start dividing Treasures into piles without using a sorting strategy?

Ask students to explain what sorting method they are using. They may have a method that is not obvious to you. Also, some students may sort using more than one attribute—for example, a pile of yellow creepy crawlers, a pile of 4-legged creepy crawlers, and a pile of short creepy crawlers. Accept any method as long as students can explain clearly how they are sorting.

► Some students don't like their Treasures and want to sort another pair's Treasures?

This is natural. Some students will prefer sorting creepy crawlers instead of tiles, for example. Plan on doing this activity with your students more than once, and tell students that they will have a chance to sort a different Treasure next time.

WHAT YOU MIGHT SEE

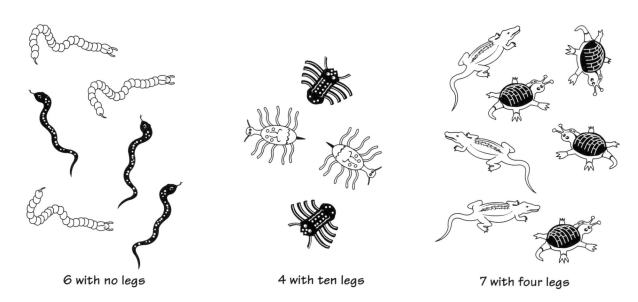

6 with no legs   4 with ten legs   7 with four legs

Some students may sort their creepy crawlers by the number of legs.

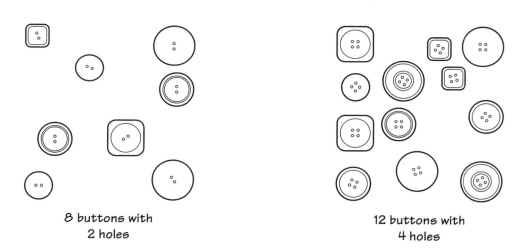

8 buttons with
2 holes

12 buttons with
4 holes

Some students may sort their buttons by the number of holes.

WHAT TO LOOK FOR IN STUDENT'S WORK

Was the student able to sort the Treasures into groups?

Was the student able to count how many Treasures were in each group?

Did the student record how she sorted the Treasures?

QUESTIONS FOR DISCUSSION

- How did you sort your Treasures? How many Treasures were in each group?

- Did anyone sort the Treasures in a different way? Tell what you did.

- Do you think there are more or fewer ways to sort the tiles than there are to sort the creepy crawlers?

- Do you think it is easier to sort the shells or the buttons by color? Tell us why.

- Do you think there are many different ways to sort the Treasures? What makes you think so?

- Of all the ways you found to sort your Treasures, which ways wouldn't work if you couldn't see them?

JOURNAL REFLECTION

Write how you sorted your Treasures.

Suppose you were going to sort your Treasures in another way. How would you do it?

QUESTION 2 How are the two buttons alike and different?

Pick any two buttons. Can you describe how the buttons are alike and how they are different? Make a drawing of your buttons. Write about how they are alike and how they are different.

MATERIALS

For each pair of students

- ■ Sorting Treasures (buttons)
- ■ paper, pencils, and crayons for recording

INTRODUCING THE QUESTION

1 Hold up two different books in front of the class. **How are these objects alike? How are they different?** On the chalkboard or overhead projector, make lists of the words the students use to describe the similarities and the differences. Leave the lists up during the activity.

2 Introduce the question. **Work with your partner. Choose any two buttons from your pile. Can you describe how your buttons are alike and how they are different? Make a drawing of your buttons. Write about how they are alike and how they are different.**

WHAT SHOULD YOU DO IF . . .

▶ Some students list only one difference and one similarity for their two buttons?

These students may think that there aren't very many differences or similarities to be found with only two objects. Encourage these students to stretch their thinking. Help students focus on the different attributes. **Describe this button to me. Can you describe this button in the same way? Explain.**

▶ Some students find only differences between the buttons?

These students may be so focused on listing all the differences, they forget to look for similarities. Remind them that they must also describe how the two buttons are alike.

▶ Some students have difficulty describing how their buttons are alike and different?

These students may not yet have the language skills needed to write how the buttons are alike and different. Encourage these students to draw pictures to show the buttons' similarities and differences.

WHAT YOU MIGHT SEE

They are both round. The orange button is bigger.

Some students may find only one similarity and one difference.

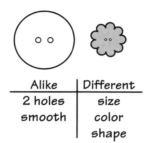

Alike	Different
2 holes	size
smooth	color
	shape

Some students may use a table to organize the similarities and differences.

WHAT TO LOOK FOR IN STUDENT'S WORK

Was the student able to find more than one similarity and one difference?

Does the student's recording show clearly the similarities and differences?

QUESTIONS FOR DISCUSSION

- In how many ways are your two buttons alike? What are the ways?

- In how many ways are your buttons different? What are the ways?

- Did anyone come up with another way to compare their two buttons? Explain the differences and similarities you found.

- Now that you have heard how others compared their buttons, could you come up with more similarities and differences between your two buttons? What are they?

JOURNAL REFLECTION

Would it be easier or more difficult to compare three buttons? Why do you think so?

Explain how you would compare the two buttons if you could not see them.

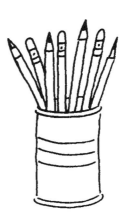

QUESTION 3

What does your pattern look like?

Use 12 Treasures to make a pattern. What does your pattern look like? Make a recording and explain your pattern.

MATERIALS

For each pair of students

- Sorting Treasures
- paper, pencils, and crayons for recording

For the overhead projector

- opaque Sorting Treasures (tiles)

INTRODUCING THE QUESTION

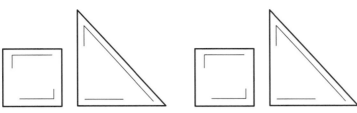

1 On the overhead projector, show the above pattern with tiles. **What comes next in the pattern?** (square tile) **How do you know? Describe this pattern. How do you know it is a pattern?**

2 After discussing what a pattern is, introduce the question. **Now it's your turn to make a pattern. Work with your partner. Use 12 Treasures to make a pattern. What does your pattern look like? Make a recording and explain your pattern.**

WHAT SHOULD YOU DO IF . . .

▶ Some students make a pattern with their Treasures but don't make a recording?

These students may be reluctant to record their pattern because they have difficulty drawing. Encourage them to think of other ways to represent the pattern they have made. They might trace the objects, for example, or devise a notation system of symbols to represent the objects in their pattern. Let these ideas come from the students.

▶ Some students quickly create the pattern and complete a clear recording of their work?

These students may need an extra challenge. Ask them to find and record as many different patterns as they can using 12 Treasures or to make a pattern using 30 Treasures.

▶ Some students make a row of Treasures with no pattern?

These students may be uncertain about what makes a pattern, or they may have arranged the Treasures into a pattern that is not obvious to you. Ask them to describe their pattern. If it's still not clear, help them practice seeing patterns with the Treasures or other objects in the classroom. Have them explain to you what makes each pattern.

WHAT YOU MIGHT SEE

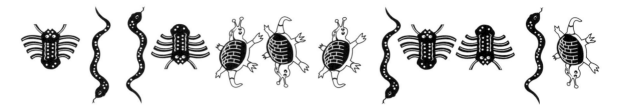

Some students may create patterns that aren't immediately obvious. It is important to have students explain what their pattern is.

Some students may create simple AB patterns.

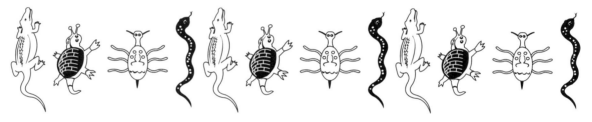

Some students may create more complex patterns.

WHAT TO LOOK FOR IN STUDENT'S WORK

Was the student able to create a pattern with the Treasures?

Did the student make a clear recording of his pattern?

Could the student explain her pattern?

QUESTIONS FOR DISCUSSION

- What pattern did you create with your Treasures? How do you know it is a pattern? What comes next in your pattern?

- Did anyone create a different pattern? Describe the pattern you created.

- How do you know when you have created a pattern?

- How are some of our patterns alike? How are they different?

- How many patterns do you think you could make with your 12 Treasures?

JOURNAL REFLECTION

Write about how you know when you have made a pattern.

Do you think it is easy or difficult to make patterns? Why do you think so?

What pattern would you make next time?

4

Can you draw a shape that can hold 30 Treasures?

Can you draw a shape that can hold exactly 30 Treasures? Draw your shape. Place your Treasures inside it. Count your Treasures to check. Make a recording using words and pictures to tell about what you did.

MATERIALS

For each pair of students

- Sorting Treasures
- paper, pencils, and crayons for recording

For the overhead projector

- opaque Sorting Treasures (creepy crawlers)

INTRODUCING THE QUESTION

1 Ask students to hold their hands out in front of them, palms facing up. **How many creepy crawlers might fit in your hand without overlapping? What makes you think so?** Give students time to share their thinking.

2 **Here's one way to find out how many creepy crawlers could fit.** Trace a volunteer's hand on the overhead projector. Have the student place as many creepy crawlers as will fit inside the outline. **How many creepy crawlers fit? How close was your guess?**

3 Introduce the question. **Do you think you can draw a shape that will hold exactly 30 Treasures? Draw your shape. Place the Treasures inside the shape. Count to check. Make a recording of what you did.**

WHAT SHOULD YOU DO IF . . .

▶ Some students gather and fit together 30 Treasures before they draw a shape to hold them?

▶ Some students focus on making shapes that could hold 30 or more Treasures, but they fill them with fewer?

▶ Some students quickly draw a shape for the Treasures and record their results?

Some students may be so concerned with being "right" that they are reluctant to guess or estimate. Remind these students that they need to draw a shape first, then check to see if it will hold exactly 30 Treasures.

These students may not have 30 Treasures inside the shape because they miscounted or because they forgot the shapes must hold exactly 30 Treasures. **How many Treasures must fit inside the shape? How many Treasures are in your shape?**

These students may need an extra challenge. Encourage them to draw another shape that will hold half as many Treasures, or have them draw three different shapes that will each hold the same number of the same kind of Treasures.

WHAT YOU MIGHT SEE

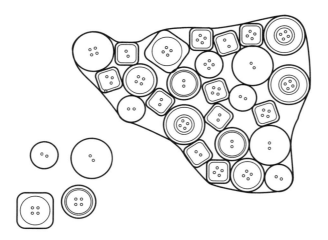

Some students may draw irregular shapes.

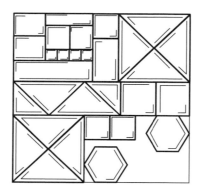

Some students may draw squares.

WHAT TO LOOK FOR IN STUDENT'S WORK

Was the student able to draw a shape that could hold about 30 Treasures?

Did the student's shape hold about 30 Treasures?

Does the student's recording explain clearly how she chose and tested a shape?

QUESTIONS FOR DISCUSSION

- Can you draw a shape that will hold exactly 30 Treasures? Explain.

- Did anyone else draw a shape that held exactly 30 Treasures? How do you know?

- What kind of shape did you draw for the creepy crawlers? Why did you choose that shape?

- What kind of shape did you draw for the shells? Why did you choose that shape?

- What kind of shape did you choose for the buttons? Why did you choose that shape?

- What kind of shape did you choose for the tiles? Why did you choose that shape?

JOURNAL REFLECTION

How might you explain this activity to someone from another class or someone at home?

Draw a shape you think will fit exactly 60 Treasures. Why do you think the shape will hold 60 Treasures?

Can you write an addition story?

Use your creepy crawlers. Can you write an addition story about them? Record your story. Write an addition equation to match.

MATERIALS

For each pair of students

- Sorting Treasures (approximately 30 creepy crawlers)
- paper, pencils, and crayons for recording

For the overhead projector

- opaque Sorting Treasures (creepy crawlers)

INTRODUCING THE QUESTION

1 Show 6 creepy crawlers on the overhead projector. **Can anyone tell me an addition story about these creepy crawlers? Can you write an addition equation to match your story?** Give students time to share their stories and to write the equations on the overhead projector. Ask students to explain how their equations match their stories.

2 Introduce the question to the class. **Work with your partner. Can you make up more addition stories using your creepy crawlers? Record one of your stories. Write an addition equation to match.**

WHAT SHOULD YOU DO IF . . .

▶ Some students do not make a recording of their addition story?

Some students may have created a complicated story that they find difficult to translate into an addition story on paper. Suggest that one partner tell the creepy crawler story while the other student records it. Other students may have difficulty with language skills. Suggest that these students record their story using pictures or diagrams.

▶ Some students create a story, but it is not an addition story?

These students may be uncertain about how to write a story that involves the operation of addition. Ask them to recall the stories that students told at the beginning of the activity. **How were the stories alike? What happened in the stories? What makes an addition story?**

WHAT YOU MIGHT SEE

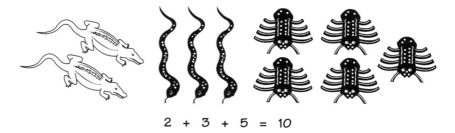

$$2 + 3 + 5 = 10$$

Some students may create stories and write equations with three or more addends.

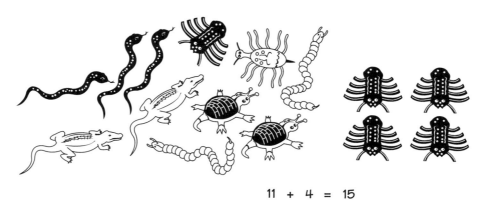

$$11 + 4 = 15$$

Some students may create stories and write equations with a two-digit addend.

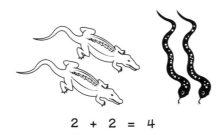

$$2 + 2 = 4$$

Some students may create simple addition stories and equations.

WHAT TO LOOK FOR IN STUDENT'S WORK

Was the student able to create an addition story using the creepy crawlers?

Was the student able to write an addition equation for his story?

Does the student's recording reflect the story she was trying to tell?

QUESTIONS FOR DISCUSSION

- Can someone share an addition story? Tell us your addition story.

- How do you know your story is an addition story?

- What addition equation did you write for your story? How did you know to write that equation?

- Did anyone come up with another addition story? Tell us about it. How do you know it's an addition story?

- What equation did you write? How does it match your story?

- How might you create another addition story using a different type of Treasure?

JOURNAL REFLECTION

Write about how you know your story is an addition story.

Write an addition story for 5 + 3 = 8.

Write an addition story for 0 + 9 = 9.

QUESTION 6 Can you write a subtraction story?

Use your creepy crawlers. Can you write a subtraction story about them? Record your story. Write a subtraction equation to match.

MATERIALS

For each pair of students

- Sorting Treasures (approximately 30 creepy crawlers)
- paper, pencils, and crayons for recording

For the overhead projector

- opaque Sorting Treasures (creepy crawlers)

INTRODUCING THE QUESTION

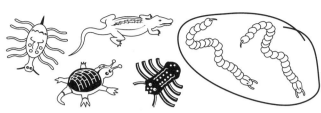

1 Show a group of 6 creepy crawlers outside a circle drawn on the overhead projector. Move 2 of the creepy crawlers inside the circle. **Can anyone tell me a subtraction story about these creepy crawlers? Can you write a subtraction equation to match your story?** Give students time to share their stories and to write the equations on the overhead projector. Ask students to explain how their equations match their stories.

2 Introduce the question to the class. **Work with your partner. Can you make up more subtraction stories using your creepy crawlers? Record one of your stories. Write a subtraction equation to match.**

WHAT SHOULD YOU DO IF . . .

► Some students focus on playing with the creepy crawlers and not on telling a subtraction story?

If students have not had much experience with creepy crawlers, they may need some free exploration time. Allow students to play with their creepy crawlers for a while. Then direct them back to the task at hand.

► Some students tell a clear creepy crawler story but have trouble writing the story and equation?

In order to write the story and equation, students must rethink the subtraction story. To do this, students must mentally put the groups of creepy crawlers back together and remember the action. This calls for a reversal of thinking, a mental ability that many students may still be developing.

► Some students don't write a complete subtraction equation?

These students may record only the first part of the equation, omitting the answer. Explain to students that an equation should tell the whole story. **Tell me your story. How does your subtraction equation tell about your story? Does your equation tell the complete story?**

WHAT YOU MIGHT SEE

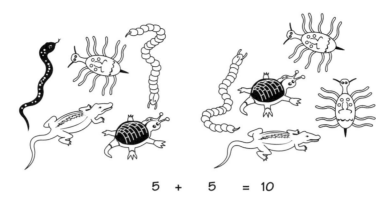

5   +   5   =   10

Some students may have trouble rethinking their story and may mistakenly write an equation that does not match their story.

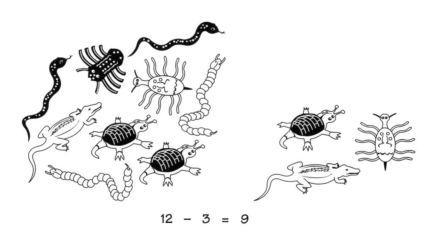

12   -   3   =   9

Some students may write a subtraction story and an equation.

WHAT TO LOOK FOR IN STUDENT'S WORK

Was the student able to create a subtraction story using the creepy crawlers?

Did the student write a subtraction equation for his story?

Does the student's recording reflect the story she created?

QUESTIONS FOR DISCUSSION

- What was the subtraction story you wrote using the creepy crawlers?

- How do you know your story is a subtraction story?

- What equation did you write for your story? How did you know what equation to write?

- Did anyone write a different subtraction story? Describe what you wrote. How do you know your story is a subtraction story?

- What was the subtraction equation you wrote to match your story? How does the equation describe what happens in the story?

- Compare a subtraction story with an addition story. How are they the same? How are they different?

JOURNAL REFLECTION

Explain how using objects like the creepy crawlers helps you to write a subtraction story and equation.

Write a subtraction story for $8 - 0 = 8$.

Is it easier to write addition or subtraction stories? Explain why.

How many creepy crawlers are hidden?

Put some creepy crawlers on your desktop. Hide some under your hand. Tell your partner how many there are in all. How many creepy crawlers are hidden? Have your partner guess. Take turns hiding creepy crawlers and guessing how many are hidden. Write a story about one of your turns. Write an equation to match.

MATERIALS

For each pair of students

- Sorting Treasures (approximately 30 creepy crawlers)
- paper, pencils, and crayons for recording

For the overhead projector

- opaque Sorting Treasures (creepy crawlers)

INTRODUCING THE QUESTION

1 Show 7 creepy crawlers on the overhead projector. **These 7 creepy crawlers went for a hike in the woods. Some of them got lost.** Turn off the overhead projector and remove 3 of the creepy crawlers. Turn the projector back on. **How many creepy crawlers got lost?** (3) **How do you know?** Give students time to explain their thinking.

2 **Can you write an equation to match the story?** Have a volunteer record the equation on the overhead projector. Retell the story if needed. **How did you know what equation to write?**

3 Introduce the question to the class. **You and your partner are going to play a hiding game with your creepy crawlers. Hide some creepy crawlers under your hand. Tell your partner how many creepy crawlers there are in all. How many creepy crawlers are hidden? Have your partner guess. Take turns hiding the creepy crawlers and guessing how many are hidden. Write a story about one of your turns. Write an equation to match.**

WHAT SHOULD YOU DO IF . . .

▶ Some students don't record one of their stories?

Students may become so involved in telling stories that they may not realize how much time has passed. Remind students that they need to record at least one of their stories.

▶ Some students write a story about the creepy crawlers that does not relate to the activity?

The connection between the games they played and the stories they are to write may not be clear to them. They may have performed the activity according to the directions even though their story does not reflect what they did. Suggest to these students that they discuss the games they played. **How might you write a story about what you did?**

WHAT YOU MIGHT SEE

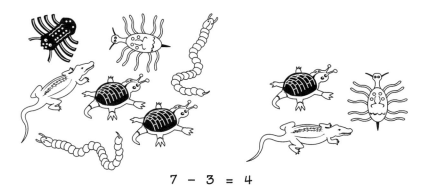

$$7 - 3 = 4$$

Some students may forget the number of creepy crawlers they started with and may write an incorrect equation for their story.

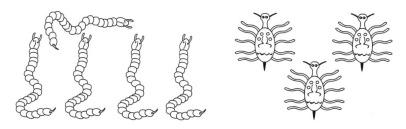

Some students may forget to write an equation.

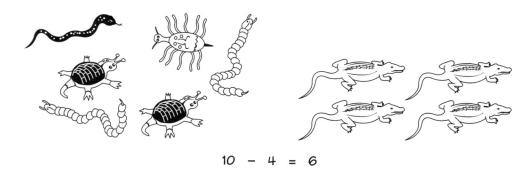

$$10 - 4 = 6$$

Some students may write a story and a matching equation.

WHAT TO LOOK FOR IN STUDENT'S WORK

Was the student able write a story about one of his turns?

Did the student write an equation to match his story?

Does the student's story reflect what she did with the creepy crawlers?

QUESTIONS FOR DISCUSSION

- What story did you write about your creepy crawlers? Tell us your story.

- Could you tell how many creepy crawlers were hidden? How did you know?

- What equation did you write to match your story? How did you know what to write?

- Did anyone create a different story with their creepy crawlers? Explain your story.

- What kinds of information did you need to include in your creepy crawler story in order for it to make sense?

JOURNAL REFLECTION

Write a story and a matching equation about a group of creepy crawlers where none are hidden.

Write about why you think it is easy or difficult to write stories about creepy crawlers.

Where do your buttons belong?

Look at the two overlapping circles. One circle is labeled "Small." The other circle is labeled "2 Holes." Where do your buttons belong? Sort the buttons. Make a recording to show where your buttons belong.

MATERIALS

For each pair of students

- Sorting Treasures (approximately 30 buttons)
- paper, pencils, and crayons for recording
- Venn Diagram reproducible (p. 82)

For the overhead projector

- opaque Sorting Treasures (tiles)

INTRODUCING THE QUESTION

1 Make a two-circle Venn diagram on the overhead projector. Label one circle "4 Sides" and the other circle "Large." Place 8 tiles—2 large tiles with 4 sides, 2 small tiles with 4 sides, 2 small round tiles, and 2 large tiles with 3 sides—on the overhead projector outside of the Venn diagram. **Where can you put these tiles?** Go through the tiles one by one, placing them where students tell you. If students have trouble determining where large, 4-sided tiles go, ask them to describe the tiles. **You said these tiles are large and have 4 sides. Could they go in this circle? What about in this circle? Where is a good place to put the tiles to show that they could go in both circles?** (in the place where the circles overlap) When you come to the small round tiles, ask similar questions until students suggest putting the tiles outside of both circles.

2 Distribute a copy of the Venn Diagram reproducible to students. **Look at the two overlapping circles.** Point out that one circle is labeled "2 Holes" and the other circle is labeled "Small." **Where do your buttons belong? Sort your buttons. Make a recording to show where your buttons belong.**

WHAT SHOULD YOU DO IF . . .

▶ Some students have trouble getting started?

These students may be unsure of how to organize the buttons to fit into the different categories. Remind them of the categories in the Venn diagram. Then suggest that they look at their buttons and describe each one. **How can you use this information to sort your buttons?**

▶ Some students begin to sort the buttons, then stop?

These students may be frustrated that some of the buttons do not seem to fit into either of the groups. Have the students describe to you how they have organized their buttons. **Which buttons go in this circle? Which buttons go in this circle? Is there a place to put buttons that are small and have two holes? Where would you put buttons that are neither small nor have two holes?**

WHAT YOU MIGHT SEE

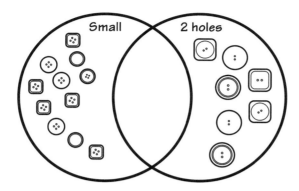

Some students may be unsure about where to put buttons that fit both categories.

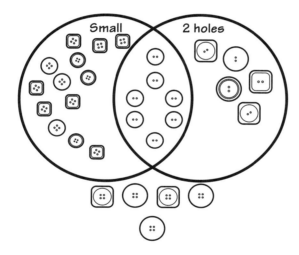

Some students may sort the buttons into the appropriate groups, using the overlapping space for buttons that fit both categories.

WHAT TO LOOK FOR IN STUDENT'S WORK

Was the student able to sort the buttons into groups and place them where they belonged?

Was the student able to make a recording of the buttons and where they belonged?

Does the student's recording clearly show his thinking?

QUESTIONS FOR DISCUSSION

- Describe how you sorted your buttons.

- Did anyone sort their buttons in a different way? How?

- Where did you put your small buttons with two holes? Why?

- Where did you put large buttons with four holes? Why?

- Where does a button with one hole go? Explain.

- Suppose you could change the labels on the circles. How might you change them so that all of your buttons would fit in the circles?

JOURNAL REFLECTION

Suppose you wanted to sort some creepy crawlers. How could you label your circles?

Which buttons did not fit in either circle?

QUESTION 9

How many Treasures do you have?

Organize your Treasures so that you can tell how many you have without counting by ones. How many Treasures do you have? Make a recording to explain how you organized your Treasures.

MATERIALS

For each pair of students

- Sorting Treasures (approximately 100)
- paper, pencils, and crayons for recording

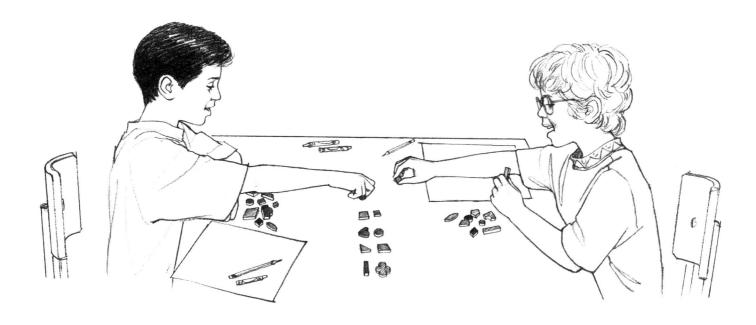

INTRODUCING THE QUESTION

1 Engage the class in a discussion about the different ways to count objects. **How might you count the number of shoes in the room without counting them one at a time? What are some other ways you could count objects without counting by ones? How did you figure that out?** Give students plenty of time to talk about different counting methods.

2 Introduce the question to the class. **Work with your partner. Organize your Treasures so you don't have to count them by ones. How many Treasures do you have? Make a recording. Explain how you organized your Treasures.**

WHAT SHOULD YOU DO IF . . .

▶ Some students organize their Treasures but still count them by ones?

Some students may not be confident with their total unless they count the Treasures by ones. Accept this method. These students may simply need more experience counting groups of objects.

▶ Some students focus on organizing the Treasures but miscalculate the number they have?

These students may organize the Treasures into groups that are not easy for them to count. For example, they may organize the objects in groups of 7 and have difficulty counting by sevens. This will be valuable information for the class discussion, when students talk about which numbers are easier to count by.

▶ Some students are uncertain about how to organize their Treasures and look to see how other groups are organizing their objects?

Some students may need reassurance on how to organize the Treasures. Encourage the students to discuss with each other how they might group the Treasures.

WHAT YOU MIGHT SEE

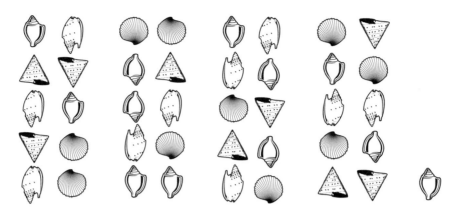

41 shells in all

Some students may quickly organize their Treasures into groups of 10.

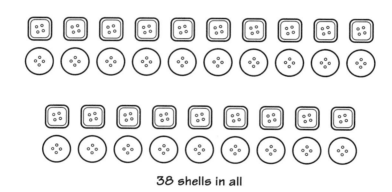

38 shells in all

Some students may organize their Treasures into groups of 2.

WHAT TO LOOK FOR IN STUDENT'S WORK

Was the student able to find the total number of Treasures?

Was the student able to organize her Treasures in order to tell how many she had without counting by ones?

Was the student able to explain clearly how he organized his Treasures?

QUESTIONS FOR DISCUSSION

- How many Treasures did you have in all?

- How did you organize your Treasures so you could tell how many you had without counting them by ones?

- Did anyone organize their Treasures in a different way? How?

- Was it easy or difficult to find the total using your way? Explain.

- Which way do you think would be easiest to find the total?

- How many ways can you organize your Treasures so you can tell how many you have without counting them by ones? What makes you think so?

JOURNAL REFLECTION

Why might it be helpful sometimes to figure out how many objects you have without counting them by ones?

How could you figure out the number of students in your class without counting them by ones?

QUESTION 10

Can you count by tens and ones?

Guess the number of Treasures you have. Can you find the total number of Treasures by counting groups of tens and ones? Make a drawing to show what you did.

MATERIALS

For each pair of students

- Sorting Treasures (approximately 100)
- paper, pencils, and crayons for recording

For the overhead projector

- opaque Sorting Treasures (23 buttons)

INTRODUCING THE QUESTION

1 Place 23 buttons on the overhead projector. **How many buttons do you think there are? How could you organize them into groups to find out?** Discuss different ways of organizing the buttons. **How could you group them by tens and ones?** Divide the buttons into groups of tens and ones as students instruct. **How many groups of ten are there?** (2) **How many groups of one are there?** (3) **How many buttons are there?** (23) **How do you know?**

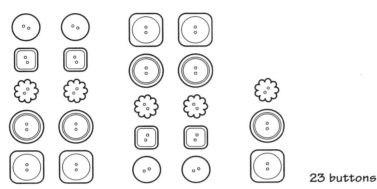

23 buttons

2 Introduce the question to the class. **Work with your partner. Find out how many Treasures you have. First, guess how many Treasures you have. Write down your guess. Then organize your Treasures into groups of tens and ones. Can you find the total number of Treasures by counting groups of tens and ones? Make a drawing to show what you did.**

WHAT SHOULD YOU DO IF . . .

▶ Some students do not estimate how many Treasures they have?

These students may be overly concerned with getting the correct answer. Reassure students that an estimate is just a best guess and that they are not looking for an exact number.

▶ Some students divide the Treasures into groups of tens and ones but find the total number by counting each one?

These students may not feel confident with their total unless they check by counting by ones. Accept this behavior. These students will feel more sure of their counting abilities after having more experience with counting by other numbers.

WHAT YOU MIGHT SEE

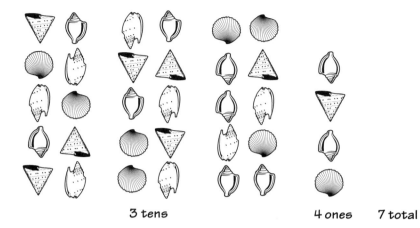

3 tens   4 ones   7 total

Some students may correctly divide the Treasures into groups of tens and ones but may count the number of groups instead of total Treasures.

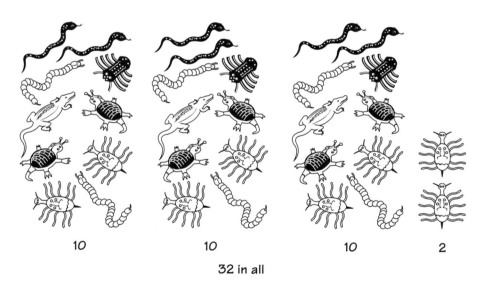

10   10   10   2

32 in all

Some students may divide their Treasures into groups of tens and ones and count them correctly.

WHAT TO LOOK FOR IN STUDENT'S WORK

Was the student able to divide the Treasures into groups of tens and ones?

Was the student able to find the total number of Treasures by counting groups of tens and ones?

Does the student's drawing reflect what she did?

QUESTIONS FOR DISCUSSION

- How many total Treasures did you guess you had?

- How many Treasures did you count?

- How did you group your Treasures before you counted them?

- How many groups of ten did you make? How many ones did you have?

- How did you count your groups of tens and ones?

- Do you think it will be easier to do a problem like this next time? Why do you think so?

JOURNAL REFLECTION

When counting groups of tens and ones, why is the number of ones always less than ten?

Suppose you divided your Treasures into groups of fours and ones instead of into groups of tens and ones. Would it be easier or more difficult to find the total number of Treasures? Why do you think so?

11 How many holes are there in all?

Sort your buttons by the number of holes. How many holes are there in all? Make a recording. Tell how you know the number of holes in all.

MATERIALS

For each pair of students

- Sorting Treasures (approximately 30 buttons)
- paper, pencils, and crayons for recording

For the overhead projector

- opaque Sorting Treasures (tiles)

INTRODUCING THE QUESTION

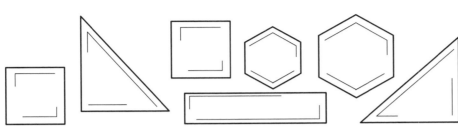

1   Show 3 four-sided tiles, 2 three-sided tiles, and 2 six-sided tiles arranged randomly on the overhead projector. **How could you sort these tiles by the number of sides?** Have a volunteer sort the tiles and explain how he arranged them.

2   Point to the four-sided group of tiles. **How many sides does each tile have in this group?** (4) **How many sides are there all together in this group?** (12) **How do you know?**

3   **Now look at all the groups. How many sides are there in all?** (30) **How do you know?**

4   Introduce the question. **Today you are going to sort your buttons by the number of holes. How many holes are there in all? Make a recording. Tell how you know the number of holes in all.**

WHAT SHOULD YOU DO IF . . .

▶ Some students sort their buttons by color and then count the number of holes in all?

Tell these students that there are many ways to sort the buttons and color is one way. Remind them that for this activity, however, it is important to sort the buttons by the number of holes.

▶ Some students sort their buttons by the number of holes, but they don't record the correct number of holes in all?

These students may be frustrated trying to count the holes one at a time. Ask them to look at the groups they have sorted and try to figure out an easier way to find how many holes there are in all. **How might you figure out the number of holes in all without counting them one by one?**

▶ Some students have trouble keeping their piles of buttons separated?

These students may have difficulty handling tiny buttons. Suggest that they use cups to hold their groups of buttons.

WHAT YOU MIGHT SEE

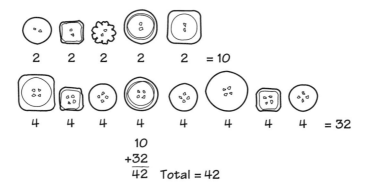

2   2   2   2   2   = 10

4   4   4   4   4   4   4   4   = 32

```
  10
 +32
 ---
  42   Total = 42
```

Some students may find the total for each group and then find the total in all.

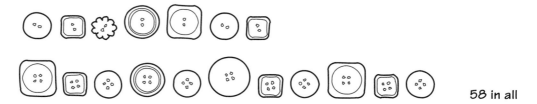

58 in all

Some students may count each hole one at a time to find the total number of holes.

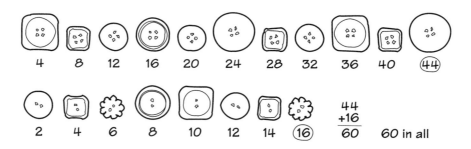

4   8   12   16   20   24   28   32   36   40   (44)

2   4   6   8   10   12   14   (16)

```
  44
 +16
 ---
  60    60 in all
```

Some students may use skip counting to find the total for each group.

WHAT TO LOOK FOR IN STUDENT'S WORK

Was the student able to sort the buttons by the number of holes?

Was the student able to find the number of holes in all?

Did the student make a clear recording and tell how he found the number of holes in all?

QUESTIONS FOR DISCUSSION

■ How many holes did you find in all? How did you find that total?

■ Did anyone find a different number of holes? How did you find that number?

■ Would you expect each pair of students to find the same number of holes for their buttons as you and your partner found for yours? Why or why not?

■ Were there more four-hole, two-hole, or one-hole buttons? Why do you think so?

JOURNAL REFLECTION

Suppose you put away all of your two-hole buttons. How many button holes would you have in all now?

Write how you could find the number of holes in all of the class's buttons.

12

How many Treasures do you need?

Suppose you want to give each person in the class 5 of your Treasures. How many Treasures do you need? Make a recording. Tell how you know how many Treasures you need.

MATERIALS

For each pair of students

■ Sorting Treasures
■ paper, pencils, and crayons for recording

For the overhead projector

■ opaque Sorting Treasures (buttons)

INTRODUCING THE QUESTION

1 Suppose you want to give 2 buttons to 3 friends. How many buttons do you need in all? (6 buttons) Give students time to work. How did you find your answer? Can someone show us on the overhead projector? Did anyone solve the problem a different way? Show us.

2 Introduce the question. Suppose you want to give 5 of your Treasures to each person in the class. How many Treasures do you need? Make a recording. Tell how you know how many Treasures you need.

3 Students will need to know the total number of students in the class to solve this problem. There are several ways to handle providing this information: Each person can count off by ones, you can write the total number on the chalkboard, or you can silently give the information to pairs as they become aware that there is missing data in the problem. Use whichever method works best for your class.

WHAT SHOULD YOU DO IF . . .

▶ Some students find an incorrect total?

These students may have set up the problem incorrectly or they may have simply miscounted. The important thing to look for in students' work is not the final answer but how they found the answer. Have students explain how they solved the problem. **How did you find your answer?**

▶ Some students become overly involved in drawing their Treasures?

These students may focus more on drawing their Treasures than on solving the problem. Bring students' attention back to the problem. **What are you working on? How will you solve the problem?**

WHAT YOU MIGHT SEE

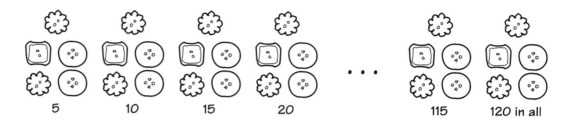

5   10   15   20   •••   115   120 in all

Some students may skip count by fives to find the total.

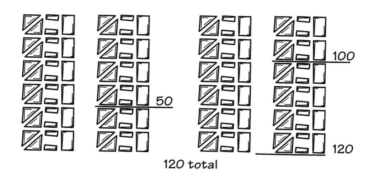

50

100

120

120 total

Some students may need to count the Treasures by ones to find the total.

‖‖‖ ‖‖‖ 10	‖‖‖ ‖‖‖ 70
‖‖‖ ‖‖‖ 20	‖‖‖ ‖‖‖ 80
‖‖‖ ‖‖‖ 30	‖‖‖ ‖‖‖ 90
‖‖‖ ‖‖‖ 40	‖‖‖ ‖‖‖ 100
‖‖‖ ‖‖‖ 50	‖‖‖ ‖‖‖ 110
‖‖‖ ‖‖‖ 60	‖‖‖ ‖‖‖ 120

120 shells

Some students may use tallies to represent Treasures and may count by tens to find the total.

WHAT TO LOOK FOR IN STUDENT'S WORK

Was the student able to find the total number of Treasures needed?

Was the student able to make a recording of her work?

Does the student's recording clearly explain how she knew how many Treasures were needed?

QUESTIONS FOR DISCUSSION

- How many of your Treasures do you need if each person in the class gets 5? How did you figure that out?

- Did anyone get a different total? Tell us how you solved the problem.

- Did anyone solve the problem in a different way? How?

- What information did you need to get started?

- Suppose you give only the girls 5 Treasures each. How many Treasures do you need? How would you solve this problem?

JOURNAL REFLECTION

Suppose you want to give 10 of your Treasures to each person in the class. How many Treasures do you need? Write how you know.

Suppose 2 new students join the class. How many Treasures do you need now? Write how you know.

13 How many Treasures does each person get?

Share your Treasures equally in your group. How many Treasures does each person get? Make a recording. Tell how you know how many each person gets.

MATERIALS

For each group of four students

- 35 Sorting Treasures
- paper, pencils, and crayons for recording

For the overhead projector

- opaque Sorting Treasures (14 tiles)

INTRODUCING THE QUESTION

1   Show 14 tiles on the overhead projector. **How many tiles are there?** (14) **Suppose 3 people want to share these tiles equally. How many tiles would each person get?** (4) **How do you know?** Have a student show how the tiles could be shared on the overhead projector.

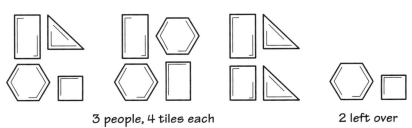

3 people, 4 tiles each   2 left over

2   Introduce the question. **Work in a group with 3 other people. Share your Treasures equally with everyone in the group. How many Treasures does each person get? Make a recording. Tell how you know how many Treasures each person gets.**

WHAT SHOULD YOU DO IF . . .

▶ Some students distribute all 35 Treasures so that not everyone has the same number?

These students may be frustrated that 35 Treasures do not divide evenly among 4 people. Emphasize the idea that with fair sharing all groups must be equal. Any pieces that cannot be shared equally are leftovers.

▶ Some students don't seem to be participating in the activity?

Suggest that the whole group discuss the problem and make sure that each person has a role. **Who will count the Treasures? Who will pass out the Treasures to each group member? Who will count the Treasures in each group?**

WHAT YOU MIGHT SEE

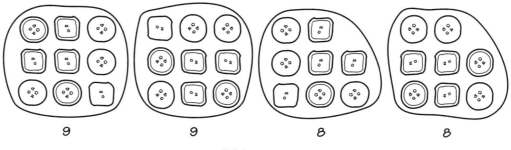

9   9   8   8

35 buttons

Some students may create unequal groups by distributing all of the Treasures.

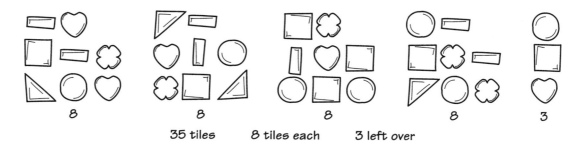

8   8   8   8   3

35 tiles   8 tiles each   3 left over

Some students may divide the 35 Treasures equally so that each person gets 8 Treasures.

WHAT TO LOOK FOR IN STUDENT'S WORK

Was the student able to share the 35 Treasures equally with a group of 4?

Was the student able to make a recording of her work?

Does the student's recording clearly tell how the group shared the Treasures?

QUESTIONS FOR DISCUSSION

- How many Treasures did each person in your group get? How did you figure that out?

- Did anyone come up with a different number? How did you figure that out?

- Did everyone in your group agree that the Treasures were shared fairly?

- Did you have any leftover Treasures? What did you do with the leftovers?

- Did you get more or fewer Treasures than you thought?

- How did your group work together to solve this problem?

JOURNAL REFLECTION

Suppose you have 15 Treasures. Show how you would share these Treasures fairly among 4 people.

Suppose you want to share the 35 Treasures equally with none left over. How many people should be in the group? How do you know?

Suppose one more person joined your group. Would you get more or fewer Treasures? How do you know?

14

How many Treasures are in each group?

Take out 60 Treasures. Divide them into 5 groups. How many Treasures are in each group? Make a recording of what you find out.

MATERIALS

For each pair of students

- 60 Sorting Treasures
- paper, pencils, and crayons for recording

For the overhead projector

- opaque Sorting Treasures (buttons)

INTRODUCING THE QUESTION

1 Show 10 buttons on the overhead projector. **How many buttons are there all together?** (10) **Let's divide them into 2 groups. How many buttons are in each group?** (5) **How do you know?** Let a volunteer show and explain how to divide the buttons.

2 Introduce the question to the class. **You and your partner will need 60 Treasures. Divide them into 5 groups. How many Treasures are in each group? Make a recording of what you find out.**

WHAT SHOULD YOU DO IF . . .

▶ Some students focus on making 5 groups but have miscounted the total number of Treasures?

Have students recheck the total number of Treasures. **How many Treasures do you need all together? How many do you have? Show me how you know.**

▶ Some students begin with the correct number of Treasures, but they do not group them correctly?

These students may have misinterpreted the instructions and may have divided the Treasures into 12 groups of 5 each. **Explain how you divided your Treasures. How are the Treasures to be divided?**

▶ Some students have difficulty managing 60 Treasures?

Encourage these students to come up with a strategy to help keep track of the Treasures. **How can you keep your Treasures from falling to the floor? What could you use to keep each of your 5 groups separate?**

WHAT YOU MIGHT SEE

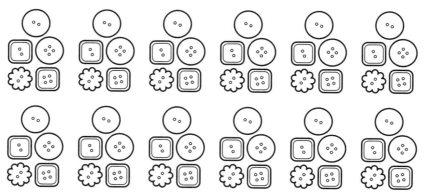

5 buttons in each group

Some students may divide the 60 Treasures into 12 groups of 5 each.

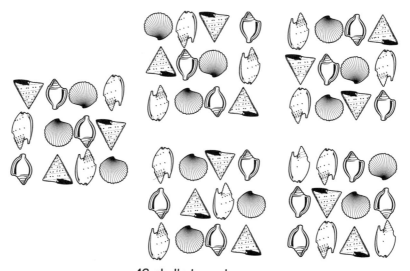

12 shells in each group

Some students may divide the 60 Treasures into 5 groups of 12 each.

WHAT TO LOOK FOR IN STUDENT'S WORK

Was the student able to divide the 60 Treasures into 5 groups of 12 each?

Was the student able to make a recording showing how he divided his Treasures?

QUESTIONS FOR DISCUSSION

- How many Treasures are in each group? How do you know?

- How did you find how many Treasures were in each group?

- Did anyone do it a different way?

- Can 60 Treasures be grouped in other ways? Describe the ways.

JOURNAL REFLECTION

Suppose you divided 60 Treasures into 12 groups. How many would be in each group? Write about how you know.

How would you divide 60 Treasures into 10 groups? How many Treasures would be in each group? Tell how you know.

QUESTION 15

How many groups are there?

Use 66 Treasures. Put your Treasures into groups of 6 Treasures each. How many groups are there? Make a recording. Write about what you did.

MATERIALS

For each pair of students

- 66 Sorting Treasures
- paper, pencils, and crayons for recording

For the overhead projector

- opaque Sorting Treasures (buttons)

INTRODUCING THE QUESTION

1 Show 8 buttons on the overhead projector. **How many buttons are there?** (8) **I want to put these buttons into groups of 2. How many groups will there be?** (4) **How do you know?** Let students work. Then have a volunteer come up and show how he solved the problem.

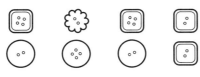

4 groups of 2

2 Introduce the question. **Work with your partner. Use 66 Treasures. Put your Treasures into groups of 6 Treasures each. How many groups are there? How do you know? Make a recording. Write about what you did.**

WHAT SHOULD YOU DO IF . . .

▶ Some students divide their Treasures into 6 groups?

These students may have misunderstood the problem, making 6 groups of Treasures not groups of 6 Treasures each. Ask students to explain what they are doing and what the problem asks. **Tell me what you are doing. How many Treasures should be in each group?**

▶ Some students have trouble managing the 66 Treasures?

These students may have difficulty keeping track of 66 Treasures or may be distracted with too many objects to work with at one time. Suggest that they figure out a way to organize their Treasures. **How can you keep track of your Treasures?**

WHAT YOU MIGHT SEE

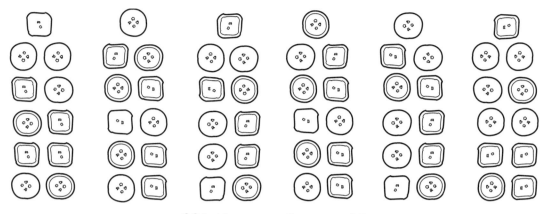

66 buttons   6 groups of 11

Some students may mistakenly divide their 66 Treasures into 6 groups of 11, not into 11 groups of 6.

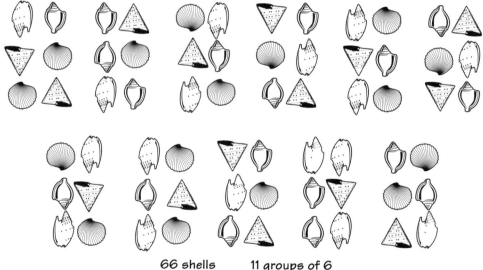

66 shells   11 groups of 6

Some students may divide the 66 Treasures into 11 groups of 6.

WHAT TO LOOK FOR IN STUDENT'S WORK

Was the student able to divide the 66 Treasures into 11 groups of 6?

Was the student able to make a recording of her work?

Does the student's recording clearly state how he divided the Treasures?

QUESTIONS FOR DISCUSSION

- How many groups did you get? How many Treasures were in each group?

- Did anyone find a different number of groups? How many Treasures were in each group?

- How did you solve this problem?

- Did anyone solve it a different way?

- Did you have any leftovers?

- Suppose you had 67 Treasures. Would you have any leftovers? What would you do?

JOURNAL REFLECTION

Suppose you put fewer than 6 Treasures in each group. Would you have more groups or fewer groups of Treasures? How do you know?

Suppose you put more than 6 Treasures in each group. Would you have more or fewer groups? How do you know?

Could you evenly divide 33 Treasures into groups of 6? Why or why not?

QUESTION 16

Which way makes more groups?

Use 47 Treasures. Divide them into groups of 10. Then divide them into groups of 8. Which way makes more groups? Make a recording. Tell what you found out.

MATERIALS

For each pair of students

- 47 Sorting Treasures
- paper, pencils, and crayons for recording

For the overhead projector

- opaque Sorting Treasures (tiles)

INTRODUCING THE QUESTION

1   Show 12 tiles on the overhead projector. **How many tiles are there all together?** (12) Divide the tiles into 3 groups of 4 each. Discuss how the tiles are grouped. **How many tiles are in each group?** (4) **How many groups are there?** (3) **Suppose I move some tiles so that there are 3 tiles in each group. How many groups are there now?** (4) **How did you figure that out?**

2   Introduce the question. **Use 47 Treasures. Divide the Treasures into groups of 10. Then divide them into groups of 8. Which way makes more groups? Make a recording. Tell what you found out.**

WHAT SHOULD YOU DO IF...

▶ Some students have difficulty making the groups of Treasures?

These students may be frustrated because they cannot divide the Treasures into even groups. There are leftovers. Encourage students to focus on how many even groups there are each time.

▶ Some students make 4 groups of 10 Treasures per group and stop?

These students may be confused about how they are to compare the groups of 10 with the groups of 8. **How many are in each group? How many groups are there? Now what happens when you divide your Treasures into groups of 8?**

WHAT YOU MIGHT SEE

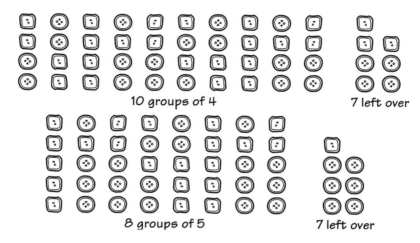

10 groups of 4   7 left over

8 groups of 5   7 left over

Some students may incorrectly divide the 47 Treasures into 10 groups and then into 8 groups.

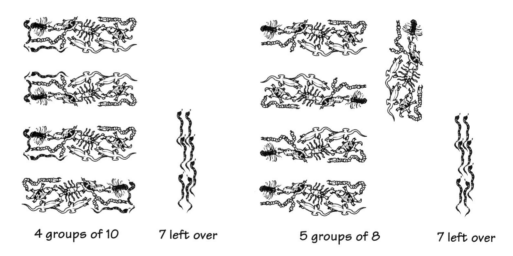

4 groups of 10   7 left over   5 groups of 8   7 left over

Some students may correctly divide the 47 Treasures into groups of 10 and groups of 8 and compare the groups.

WHAT TO LOOK FOR IN STUDENT'S WORK

Was the student able to divide the Treasures into groups of 10?

Was the student able to divide the Treasures into groups of 8?

Was the student able to determine that there were more groups of 8?

Was the student able to make a recording of what he found out?

QUESTIONS FOR DISCUSSION

- How many groups of 10 did you make? How many groups of 8 did you make?

- Which way made the most groups? How did you figure that out?

- Describe what your groups looked like when you divided the 47 Treasures into groups of 10.

- Describe what your groups looked like when you divided the 47 Treasures into groups of 8.

- What would be the fewest number of groups you could make with 47 Treasures? How do you know?

- What would be the greatest number of groups you could make with 47 Treasures? How did you figure that out?

JOURNAL REFLECTION

Suppose you divided your 47 Treasures into groups of 5. Would there be more or fewer groups than groups of 10? Would there be more or fewer groups than groups of 8? How do you know?

Suppose you divided 100 Treasures, instead of 47 Treasures, into groups of 10 and groups of 8. Would that change which way makes more groups? Explain.

17
Will the total be the same or different?

Take 19 buttons. Add 11 more. How many buttons do you have in all? Suppose you start with 11 buttons and add 19 more. Will the total be the same or different? Make a recording. Explain how you know if the total is the same or different.

MATERIALS

For each pair of students

■ Sorting Treasures (buttons)
■ paper, pencils, and crayons for recording

INTRODUCING THE QUESTION

1 Hold up 3 fingers. Hold up 5 more. How many fingers are there in all? (8) How did you figure that out?

2 Suppose you hold up 5 fingers first. Then you add 3 more. Will the total be the same as before? (yes) Explain your thinking.

3 Introduce the question to the class. Use your buttons. Take out 19 of them. Then add 11 more. How many buttons do you have in all? Suppose you start with 11 buttons and add 19 more. Will the total be the same or different? Make a recording of your work. Explain how you know if the total is the same or different.

WHAT SHOULD YOU DO IF . . .

▶ Some students do not make a recording?

These students may not be sure how to show on paper what they did with the buttons. Ask them to tell you how they found their answer. **Describe to me what you did. How can you show that on paper?**

▶ Some students do not get the same total?

These students may have miscounted. Have them explain how they found each total. In the process of going over their own work, they may discover their error. **How did you find the totals?**

WHAT YOU MIGHT SEE

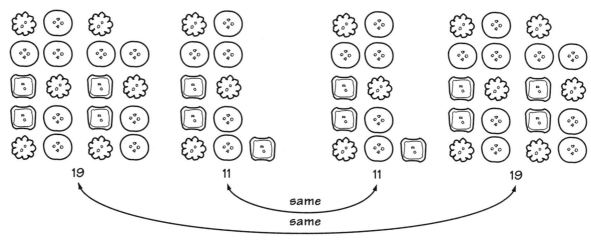

19   11   11   19

same

same

Total is the same.

Some students may conclude that because the groups are the same, the totals must be the same.

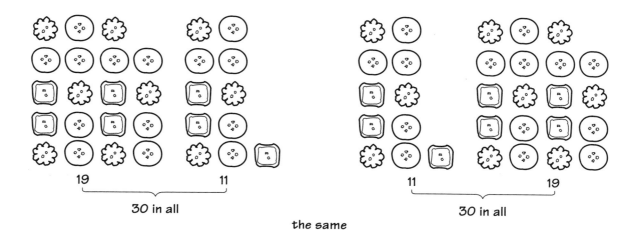

19   11   11   19

30 in all   30 in all

the same

Some students may correctly find that the totals are the same.

WHAT TO LOOK FOR IN STUDENT'S WORK

Did the student find that the totals are the same?

Was the student able to make a recording that reflected what she did with the buttons?

QUESTIONS FOR DISCUSSION

- You have 19 buttons and add 11 more. How many buttons are there?

- You have 11 buttons and add 19. Is the total the same?

- How did you solve this problem?

- Did anyone solve it a different way? Explain what you did.

- Were you surprised that the sums were the same? Why or why not?

JOURNAL REFLECTION

Suppose you have 100 buttons and add 3 more. Is it the same total if you have 3 buttons and add 100 more? Why or why not?

Suppose you have 10 buttons and add 5 more. Suppose your friend has 5 buttons. How many more buttons does your friend need to have the same total? Tell how you know.

Do you have the same number?

Show 6 groups of 4 shells. How many shells do you have in all? Suppose you have 4 groups of 6 shells. Do you have the same number of shells? Make a recording. Explain how you know if it is the same number or not.

MATERIALS

For each pair of students

- Sorting Treasures (shells)
- paper, pencils, and crayons for recording

For the overhead projector

- opaque Sorting Treasures (buttons)

INTRODUCING THE QUESTION

1 Place 6 buttons in 3 groups of 2 on the overhead projector. **How many groups of buttons are there?** (3) **How many are in each group?** (2) **What is the total number?** (6)

2 Introduce the question to the class. **Use your shells. Make 6 groups of 4 shells. How many shells do you have in all? Suppose you have 4 groups of 6 shells. Do you have the same number of shells? Make a recording. Explain how you know if it is the same number or not.**

WHAT SHOULD YOU DO IF . . .

▶ Some students have difficulty keeping the groups separated and miscount?

Suggest that students figure out a way to organize the groups of shells. They might draw circles on a sheet of paper and put the shells inside them, or they might put the shells into cups to keep them separated. Have these ideas come from students.

▶ Some students quickly determine that 6 groups of 4 shells is the same as 4 groups of 6?

These students may need an extra challenge. Encourage them to make similar groupings with different combinations of shells. **Do you see a pattern?**

WHAT YOU MIGHT SEE

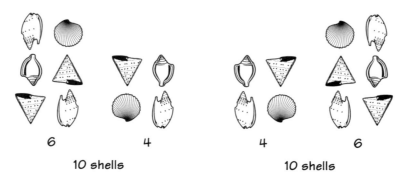

6   4   4   6

10 shells   10 shells

the same

Some students may be confused about how to group the shells correctly.

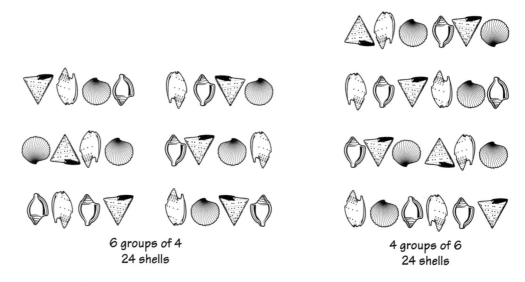

6 groups of 4
24 shells

4 groups of 6
24 shells

Some students may show that 6 groups of 4 shells and 4 groups of 6 shells have the same total number of shells.

WHAT TO LOOK FOR IN STUDENT'S WORK

Was the student able to show that 6 groups of 4 shells is the same total as 4 groups of 6 shells?

Was the student able to make a recording of his work?

QUESTIONS FOR DISCUSSION

■ How did you group your shells?

■ Is the total the same for 6 groups of 4 shells as it is for 4 groups of 6 shells? How do you know?

■ Did anyone find the answer a different way?

■ Did your findings surprise you? Why or why not?

■ Do you think 6 groups of 0 shells is the same as 0 groups of 6 shells? Why or why not?

JOURNAL REFLECTION

Is 100 groups of 5 shells the same as 5 groups of 100 shells? Tell how you know.

Six groups of 2 shells is the same as 2 groups of ___ shells. Tell how you know.

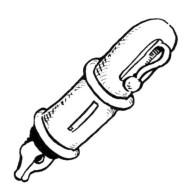

QUESTION 19 How many tiles are left?

Count out 43 tiles. Take away 25 of them. How many tiles are left? Is it the same if you had 25 tiles and tried to take away 43? Make a recording. Explain how you know if it is the same or not.

MATERIALS

For each pair of students

- Sorting Treasures (tiles)
- paper, pencils, and crayons for recording

INTRODUCING THE QUESTION

1 Engage the class in a discussion about subtraction. **Hold up 10 fingers. Take away 5 of them. How many are left?** (5) **How do you know?**

2 Introduce the question to the class. **Count out 43 tiles. Take away 25 of them. How many are left? Is it the same if you had 25 tiles and tried to take away 43? Make a recording. Explain how you know if it is the same or not.**

WHAT SHOULD YOU DO IF . . .

▶ Some students use the incorrect operation to solve the problem?

These students may be adding instead of subtracting. They may conclude that the two problems are the same. Ask students to tell you what they are doing. **How many tiles did you start with? Then what did you do? What happens when you take away 25 tiles? Now see what happens when you try to take 43 tiles away from 25.**

▶ Some students do not make a recording?

These students may not be sure how to record the second half of the problem. **Tell me what happened when you took 25 tiles away from 43. How would you write about that? What happened when you tried to take 43 from 25?** Encourage them to record what they found out.

WHAT YOU MIGHT SEE

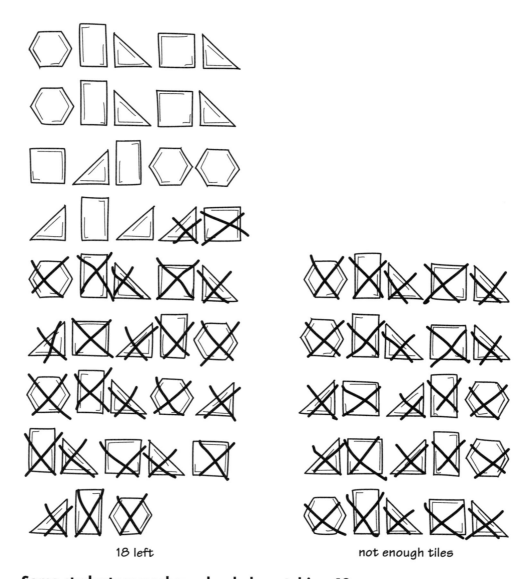

18 left

not enough tiles

Some students may show clearly how taking 43 away from 25 is not the same as taking 25 away from 43.

WHAT TO LOOK FOR IN STUDENT'S WORK

Was the student able to show that taking 43 away from 25 is not the same as taking 25 away from 43?

Did the student make a clear recording to show what he did?

QUESTIONS FOR DISCUSSION

- How many tiles did you have left when you took 25 away from 43?

- What happened when you took 43 from 25?

- Is taking 43 away from 25 the same as taking 25 away from 43? Tell how you know.

- Did you have any trouble recording what you found? What did you do?

- Is taking 43 away from 0 the same as taking 0 away from 43? Tell how you know.

JOURNAL REFLECTION

How might you explain this problem to someone at home?

Were you surprised that the two problems weren't the same? Why or why not?

Is it the same?

Divide 18 shells into 6 equal groups. How many shells are in each group? Is it the same as dividing 6 shells into 18 groups? Make a recording. Explain how you know if it is the same or not.

MATERIALS

For each pair of students

■ Sorting Treasures (shells)

■ paper, pencils, and crayons for recording

For the overhead projector

■ opaque Sorting Treasures (buttons)

INTRODUCING THE QUESTION

1 Show 8 buttons on the overhead projector. **How many buttons are there all together?** (8) **How could you divide the buttons into 4 equal groups?** Group the buttons as the students instruct. **How many are in each group?** (2) **How do you know?**

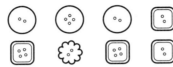

2 Introduce the question. **Work with your partner. Divide 18 of your shells into 6 equal groups. How many shells are in each group? Is it the same as dividing 6 shells into 18 groups? Make a recording. Explain how you know if it is the same or not.**

WHAT SHOULD YOU DO IF . . .

▶ Some students divide the 18 shells into 6 equal groups and then stop?

These students may be frustrated with the idea of trying to divide 6 shells into 18 equal groups. Have students tell you what they found out. **Tell me what you did. How can you record that?**

▶ Some students make 3 groups of 6 shells instead of 6 groups of 3?

These students may have misinterpreted the instructions for the activity and put 6 shells in each group, instead of dividing the shells into 6 equal groups. Ask students to tell you how they are grouping the shells. **How many shells are in each group if you divide them into 6 equal groups?**

▶ Some students do not make 6 equal groups?

These students may have miscounted the shells initially. **How many shells do you have? How many shells do you need?** Allow students to adjust their pile so that they have 18 shells. **Now can you divide them into equal groups?**

WHAT YOU MIGHT SEE

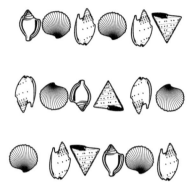

Some students may divide the shells into groups of 6 instead of into 6 equal groups.

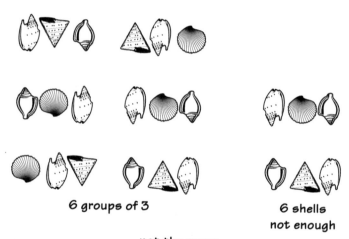

6 groups of 3

not the same

6 shells
not enough

Some students may show that 18 divided into 6 equal groups is not the same as 6 divided into 18 equal groups.

WHAT TO LOOK FOR IN STUDENT'S WORK

Was the student able to show that 18 divided into 6 equal groups is not the same as 6 divided into 18 equal groups?

Was the student able to make a clear recording of her findings?

QUESTIONS FOR DISCUSSION

■ Is 18 shells divided into 6 equal groups the same as 6 shells divided into 18 equal groups? Why or why not?

■ How did you use your shells to solve this problem?

■ Did anyone solve the problem a different way?

■ What happened when you tried to divide 6 shells into 18 equal groups?

■ How did you and your partner work together to solve this problem?

JOURNAL REFLECTION

Write to a friend. Tell them how you solved this problem.

Do you think that 10 shells divided into 5 equal groups is the same as 5 shells divided into 10 equal groups? Explain how you know.

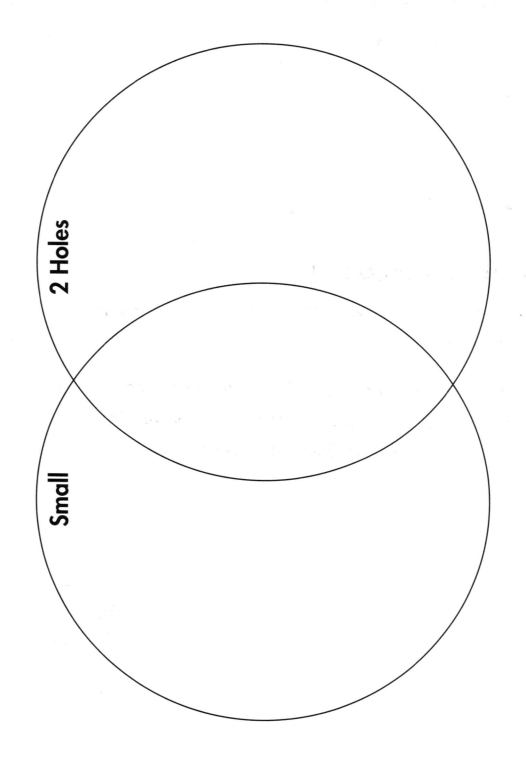

2 Holes

Small